SYSTEMATIC ME

POEMS AND PLAYS ABOUT THE HUMAN BODY

Brod Bagert's HeART of Science
www.brodbagertsheartofscience.com

A word from Brod — Your amazing human body.

Your body is the most complicated thing on earth. It controls its own temperature, defends itself from constant attack by millions of tiny enemies, repairs itself, and reproduces. It turns food and air into fuel, delivers that fuel to trillions of cells, and gets rid of the waste. It walks, runs, talks, and does cartwheels. And, even more amazing than all of these, it thinks, it creates, it remembers, and it communicates. And the amazing bundle of tissues and chemicals and electrical impulses that does all that stuff is YOU, which is why I think you're going to like getting to know a little more about how it all works.

Here's a quick summary of what you're about to learn. There are two kinds of things that make your body work: systems and organs. Each system does a particular kind of work to keep your body alive, and organs are the things each system uses to get its work done. Some organs work for more than one system. Your lungs, for example, work for three of your systems: your respiratory system because they breathe for you, your circulatory system because they supply oxygen to your bloodstream, and your excretory system because they get rid of the carbon dioxide waste that your body doesn't use.

For most of you this book will be a fun way to learn the basics of how your body works. For some of you it may be the beginning of a lifelong journey. So get ready! Either way your body is simply amazing, and this book is going to make learning about it fun and easy.

TABLE OF CONTENTS

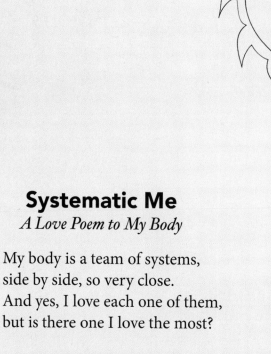

Systematic Me

A Love Poem to My Body

My body is a team of systems,
side by side, so very close.
And yes, I love each one of them,
but is there one I love the most?

My Skeletal System?
> My frame of bones, how I love you.
> O-yes-o-yes I really do.
> Without my sturdy skeleton
> I'd be a bowl of gelatin.

My Muscular System?
> Muscles-muscles, I love you,
> and if you do not think it's true,
> it isn't hard for me to prove,
> without your help I couldn't move.

My Integumentary System?
> My skin! My skin! I love you, too.
> You'll never know how much I do.
> You cover me from toe to head,
> without you I would soon be dead.

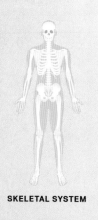

SKELETAL SYSTEM

MUSCULAR SYSTEM

INTEGUMENTARY SYSTEM

My Digestive System?
        Decomposition, I love you,
        oh how I love that thing you do.
        You work so hard, you work so long,
        converting food to keep me strong.

My Respiratory System?
        Breathing-breathing, I love you.
        I'm sure you know how much I do.
        No body ever disagreed
        that oxygen is what I need.

My Circulatory System?
        Flowing blood, how I love you.
        Delivery is what you do.
        The air I breathe, the food I eat,
        a heart that never fails to beat.

DIGESTIVE SYSTEM

RESPIRATORY SYSTEM

CIRCULATORY SYSTEM

EXCRETORY SYSTEM

IMMUNE SYSTEM

NERVOUS SYSTEM

My Excretory System?
    Excreting waste is what you do,
    and that is why I so love you.
    Without you, oh what would I be?
    A swollen bag of salt and pee.

My Immune System?
    You're my hero, yes you are.
    You fight that long internal war.
    You kill bad germs, oh yes-siree,
    and keep those germs from killing me.

My Nervous System?
    Neuron cells, how I love you!
    How could it ever not be true?
    Because of you I feel, I know,
    my brain completely runs the show.

My Endocrine System?
  Oh gentle glands, my hormone sun,
  great stimulus yet softly done—
  my growth...my mood...metabolism.
  Yes, even my eroticism.

My Reproductive System?
  Man and woman, hand in glove,
  reproducing by their love.
  A little me! A little you!
  Oh how I love that thing you do.

A favorite I could never choose,
I love them all, it's plain to see,
'cause all together they're a team,
a team that's all together me.

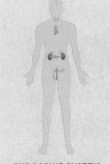

ENDOCRINE SYSTEM

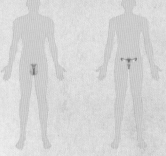

MALE REPRODUCTIVE SYSTEM   **FEMALE REPRODUCTIVE SYSTEM**

I'd like to clear something up in advance so you don't feel confused as you read more about the human body. Eventually you'll come across references to two systems that are not mentioned in this poem: the "lymphatic system" and the "urinary system."

Just remember that there *really* is a lymphatic system, but it's part of the immune system. And there certainly is a urinary system, but it's part of the overall excretory system.

Sleeping with a Skeleton

There's a skeleton in my bed,
it's as quiet as can be,
and we sleep together every night,
that skeleton and me.

Bones and joints and cartilage,
a scary work of art,
with ligaments and tendons
so it doesn't fall apart.

A skull all full of skeleton teeth
each one a different size,
with a single hole for the skeleton nose
and two for the skeleton eyes.

It's covered up with muscle and skin,
which makes it hard to see,
but it's always right there in my bed
right there inside of me.

I sleep with a skeleton every night.
Don't laugh, you know it's true.
There's a skeleton inside of me,
just like the one in you.

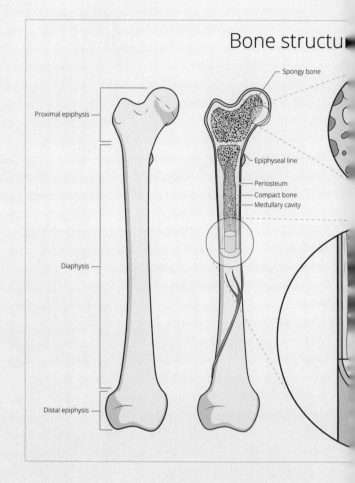

Bone structu[re]

- Spongy bone
- Proximal epiphysis
- Epiphyseal line
- Periosteum
- Compact bone
- Medullary cavity
- Diaphysis
- Distal epiphysis

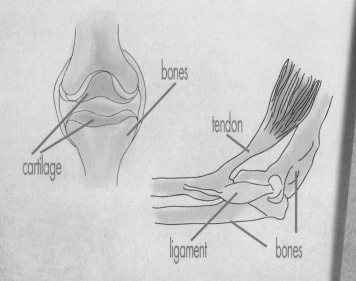

bones
cartilage
tendon
ligament
bones

Here are three words you'll want to know when you're talking about the "musculo-skeletal" system: ligament, tendon, and cartilage.
- **Ligament** is a stretchy band of tissue that connects bone to bone and keeps your joints from wobbling.
- **Tendon** is a band of tissue that connects muscle to bone.
- **Cartilage** is a soft, squishy padding that keeps your bones from grinding on each other.

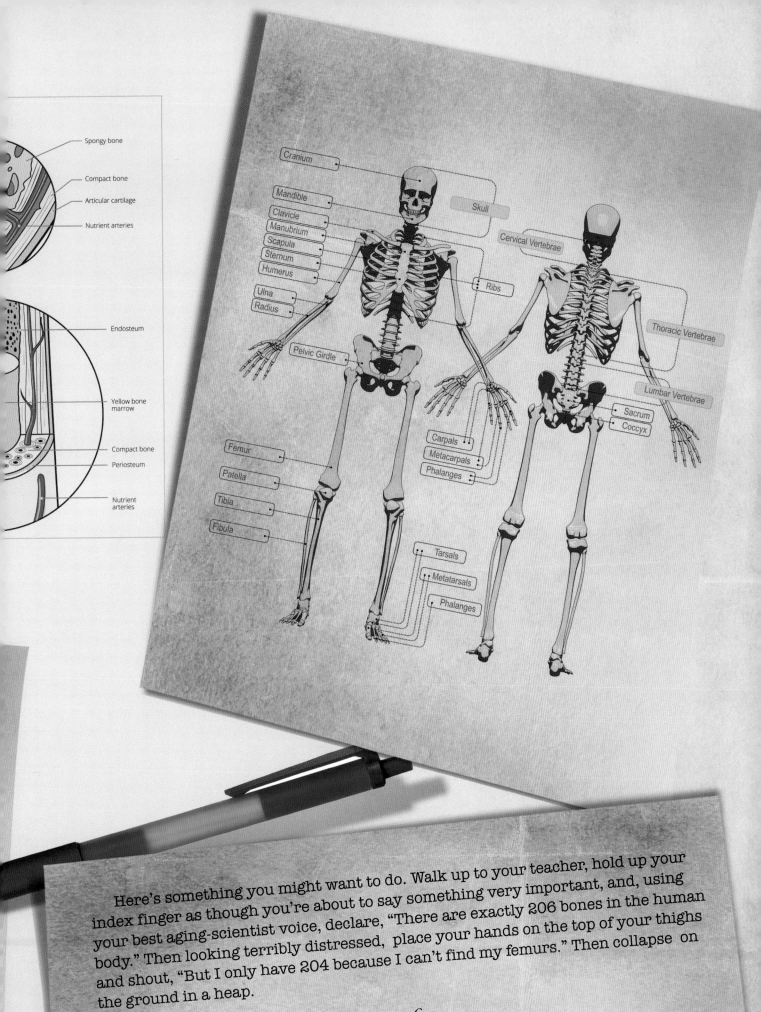

Spongy bone

Compact bone

Articular cartilage

Nutrient arteries

Endosteum

Yellow bone marrow

Compact bone

Periosteum

Nutrient arteries

Cranium

Mandible

Clavicle

Manubrium

Scapula

Sternum

Humerus

Ulna

Radius

Skull

Cervical Vertebrae

Ribs

Thoracic Vertebrae

Pelvic Girdle

Lumbar Vertebrae

Sacrum

Coccyx

Carpals

Metacarpals

Phalanges

Femur

Patella

Tibia

Fibula

Tarsals

Metatarsals

Phalanges

Here's something you might want to do. Walk up to your teacher, hold up your index finger as though you're about to say something very important, and, using your best aging-scientist voice, declare, "There are exactly 206 bones in the human body." Then looking terribly distressed, place your hands on the top of your thighs and shout, "But I only have 204 because I can't find my femurs." Then collapse on the ground in a heap.

The Largest Human Organ?

I have follicles for growing hair,
a little or a lot.
I have glands to make you sweaty
when it gets a little hot.

I have blood to keep you cool,
and fat to keep you warm,
and nerves to let you know
when you're headed into harm.

I have oil to make you waterproof,
so swimming can be fun.
I even change my color
to protect you from the sun.

If you look around your body
you will see me everyplace—
on your hands, on your feet,
on your belly, on your face.

I've always got you covered,
always there through thick and thin.
I'm the biggest organ of them all.
You know me as your…SKIN!

EPIDERMIS

7

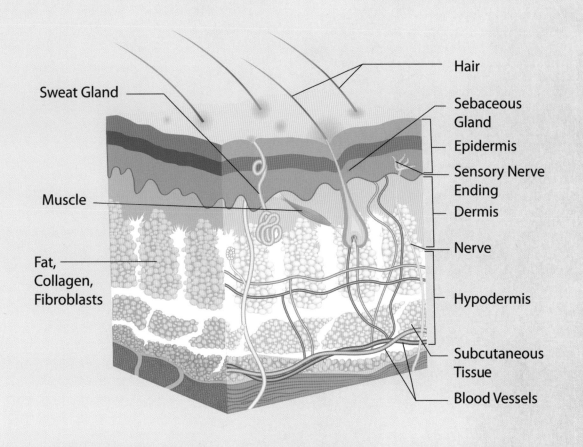

Hair

Sweat Gland

Sebaceous Gland

Epidermis

Sensory Nerve Ending

Muscle

Dermis

Nerve

Fat, Collagen, Fibroblasts

Hypodermis

Subcutaneous Tissue

Blood Vessels

This note is about the origin of words. At first, it may seem a little advanced, but it's really very easy to understand and once you get it, you'll be the master of what other people might think of as "big words" and "scientific terms."

Lots of scientific terms come from Latin or Greek which were the languages of learning in the middle ages. The scientific term for the outer layer of your skin is **epidermis**, which comes from two Greek words - **epi** (επι) which means *upon* and **derma** (δερμα) which means *skin*.

Here's another one. A hypodermic needle is what the doctor uses to give you a shot which injects medicine under the skin. So what do you think the origin of **hypodermic** might be? You already know that the **dermic** part of that word comes from the Greek word derma, which means *skin*, but what about hypo? Any guesses? It comes for the Greek word **hypo** (ὑπό), which means *under* and derma which means *skin*. So **hypodermic** means *under the skin.*

The Cookie Journey

I'm just a cookie on a plate
awaiting every cookie's fate.
Someone bit me! Oh the fear!
Holy smoke, it's dark in here!

Tooth enamel, sharp and white,
tearing, grinding, left and right.
Saliva swishing all around.
Oh no! I think I'm going down!

This esophagus thing is a very tight space.
It starts in a neck right under a face.
A muscle-squeezing kind of hose
that deep into a stomach goes.

Feel the acid! Feel the burn!
This stomach has begun to churn.
I'm turning to liquid! I'm turning to gas!
Digestion progression is terribly fast!

I'm flowing now in a gooey soup
through small intestine, loop-d-loop!
Now large intestine...the colon...at last...
I'm turning back to solid mass.

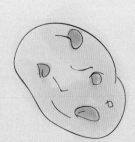

But something has begun to smash,
and now I'm falling…falling…SPLASH!
I'm floating in a big white well.
Oh disgusting! What's that smell?

It's what our bodies love to do—
Turning cookies into poo.

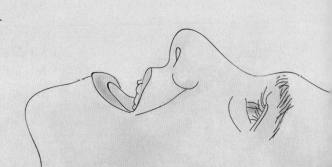

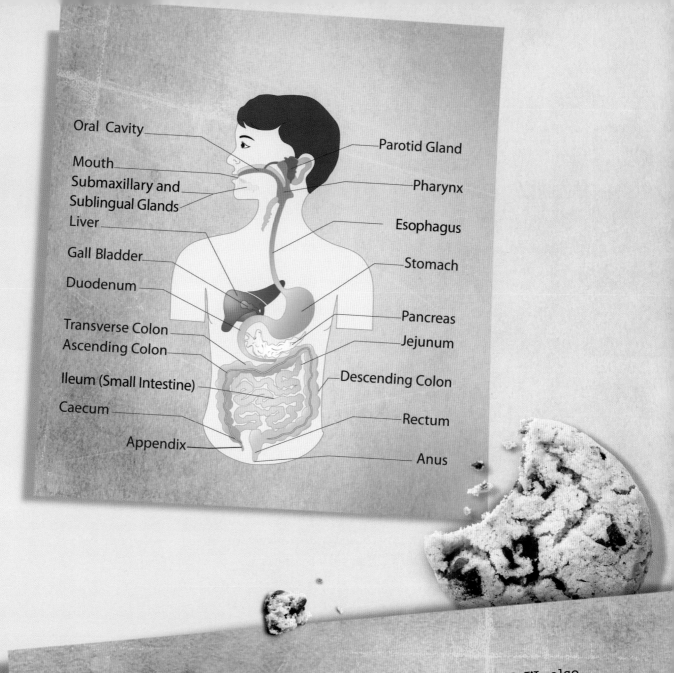

Oral Cavity

Mouth

Submaxillary and
Sublingual Glands

Liver

Gall Bladder

Duodenum

Transverse Colon

Ascending Colon

Ileum (Small Intestine)

Caecum

Appendix

Parotid Gland

Pharynx

Esophagus

Stomach

Pancreas

Jejunum

Descending Colon

Rectum

Anus

Acid is not the only thing our stomachs have to digest food. We also have enzymes and something scientists call probiotics. Enzymes are chemicals our bodies produce that act as catalysts to speed up the chemical reactions. And probiotics? (This is my favorite part.) Probiotics are bacteria! That's right, the same kind of living organisms that cause disease, except instead of making us sick these bacteria are good for us. That's why scientists call them probiotics, using the Latin prefix *pro* which means *on behalf of*. Together these three elements cause biochemical reactions that turn the food we eat into nutrients that can be absorbed into our bloodstream.

Here's another cool word. The opposite of probiotic bacteria would be pathogenic bacteria, the ones that cause disease. The word **pathogen** comesfrom two Greek words: **pathos** (πάθος) which means *suffering* or *disease*, and **genesis** (γένεσις) which means *origin*.

The Silent Voice of Fight or Flight
or
Being Chased by a Monster

My body does this crazy thing
that feels a bit traumatic.
I don't decide to do it,
my response is automatic.

Run-run! Flee-flee!
A hungry monster's chasing me!
Lungs breathe! Heart beat!
Move legs! Move feet!

Respiration, circulation
help with human animation.
Through nose and mouth and past my tongue.
the air goes down into each lung.
Into my blood and through my heart
and out to every body part.

Lungs breathe! Heart beat!
Move legs! Move feet!
Run-run! Flee-flee!
A HUNGRY MONSTER'S CHASING ME!

Something takes control, and I'm
on automatic drive—
the voice of fight or flight that keeps
us humans beings alive.

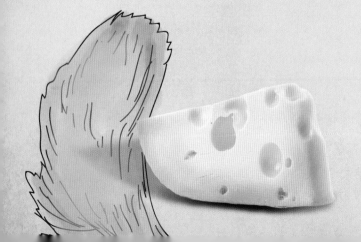

This poem is about a cool thing your body does when you get scared. It happens automatically and is one of the things that has helped humans survive in a dangerous world. Scientists call it the "acute stress" or "fight or flight" response. It happens when part of your nervous system tells your adrenal gland to release adrenaline and norepinephrine into your bloodstream and POW!

Your heart rate increases, your muscles tense, you breathe faster, your vision changes and sometimes you even hear better. It takes about two to three minutes for your body to respond to the threat and 20 to 60 minutes for your body to return to normal after the threat is over.

Blood Flow in Human Circulatory System

blood flow to head and arms

superior vena cava

pulmonary arteries

pulmonary veins

heart

aorta

inferior vena cava

blood flow to digestive system and lower limbs

Human Respiratory System

bronchus

pulmonary arteriole

pulmonary venule

trachea (windpipe)

upper lobe

heart

lower lobe

alveoli

diaphragm

Respiratory Failure

Today we studied the respiratory system:
    The diaphragm contracts,
    air moves through the trachea into the lungs
    where blood gathers oxygen,
    flows up the pulmonary artery,
    back through the heart
    and out to the rest of the body.
Today we studied the respiratory system,
and mine was working fine
until Derrick Wood walked up to me and said hello,
and as I gazed into his eyes...
    My diaphragm did not contract,
    no air flowed through my trachea,
    my alveoli took a vacation,
    and my body screamed for oxygen.
I'm feeling better now,
but I've got one thing to say:
Derrick Wood, you hunk of a man,
YOU TAKE MY BREATH AWAY!

Breathing is one of the things your body does without you having to think about it, what scientists call an "involuntary action." The things we absolutely have to do to stay alive, like breathing and heart rate, are all involuntary and are controlled by a part of your brainstem called (get ready for a very cool word) your medulla oblongata. We'll learn more about the famous Miss Medulla later on in this book.

Ins and Outs of the Human Heart
or
The Difference Between Arteries and Veins

I know they're not the same,
but I've got one little glitch.
Sure, I know they're different,
but I don't know which is which.

Which one moves blood away from the heart?
Arteries? Right? I am totally smart.
So the other's the one that must bring the blood back
which has got to be veins, it's a matter of fact.

So raise your fist and give a shout.
VEINS IN! ARTERIES OUT!
Yes that's the way it's always been.
ARTERIES OUT! VEINS IN!

There are ther differences between arteries and veins. **ARTERIES** carry oxygenated blood (except for the pulmonary artery and umbilical artery). **VEINS** carry deoxygenated blood (except for pulmonary veins and umbilical vein).

The pathway of blood flow through the heart

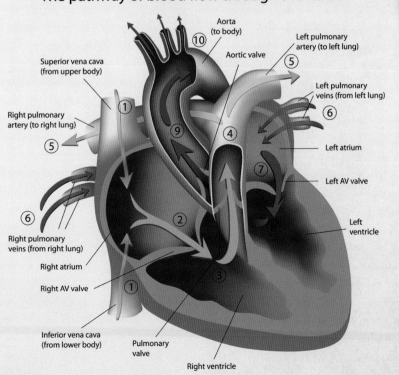

Superior vena cava (from upper body)

Right pulmonary artery (to right lung)

Right pulmonary veins (from right lung)

Right atrium

Right AV valve

Inferior vena cava (from lower body)

Pulmonary valve

Right ventricle

Aorta (to body)

Aortic valve

Left pulmonary artery (to left lung)

Left pulmonary veins (from left lung)

Left atrium

Left AV valve

Left ventricle

ARTERIES have a thick, elastic layer of muscle to withstand the pressure of blood being pumped by the heart.
VEINS have a thin, elastic layer of muscle with valves that stop the blood from flowing backwards.

The Heartbeat Squad

Protecting you right from the start,
like soldiers working in your heart,
and if that sounds a little odd,
it's time you meet the heartbeat squad.
So let's all have a little fun.
Soldiers! Sound off one by one!

"**Vena Cava**, SIR!
I am the largest vein in the human body,
I carry deoxygenated blood
into the right atrium of the heart.
READY FOR DUTY, SIR!"

"**Right atrium**, SIR!
I am first of the four chambers of the heart.
Deoxygenated blood enters through me,
and I pump it into the next chamber.
READY FOR DUTY, SIR!"

"**Right ventricle**, SIR!
The second of the four chambers of the heart.
Deoxygenated blood comes through me,
and I pump it into the pulmonary artery.
READY FOR DUTY, SIR!"

When I was little, we used to have a cartoon on TV where this little-bitty Mighty Mouse would lift gigantic stuff like elephants and houses. When I think about the human heart it always reminds me of Mighty Mouse. Your heart is only about the size of your fist but it beats 100,000 times a day, pumps 2,000 gallons of blood through 60,000 miles of veins and arteries, and it never gets a vacation. Mighty Mouse!

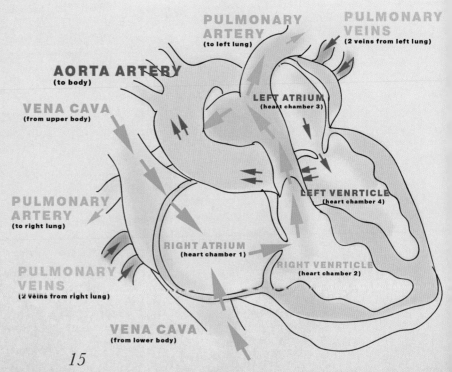

15

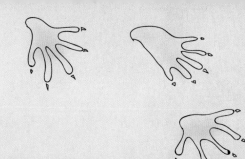

"**Pulmonary artery**, SIR!
I carry deoxygenated blood from the heart to the lungs,
the only artery that carries deoxygenated blood,
and I AM READY FOR DUTY, SIR!"

"**Pulmonary veins**, SIR!
There are four of us,
two from the left lung and two from the right,
and we carry oxygenated blood back to the heart,
the only veins that carry oxygenated blood,
and WE ARE READY FOR DUTY, SIR!"

"**Left atrium**, SIR!
I am third of the four chambers of the heart.
Oxygenated blood comes through me,
and I pump it to the next chamber.
READY FOR DUTY, SIR!"

"**Left ventricle**, SIR!
I am last of the four chambers of the heart.
Oxygenated blood comes through me,
and I pump it out to the aorta.
READY FOR DUTY, SIR!"

"**Aorta artery**, SIR!
The largest human artery,
I carry oxygenated blood
from the heart to the rest of the body,
and I...AM...READY FOR DUTY, SIR!

Like soldiers working in your heart,
protecting you right from the start.
Heartbeat Squad! You're the best!
You work and work and never rest!

The PP Twins
or
Glory of the Golden Stream
A Play In One Act

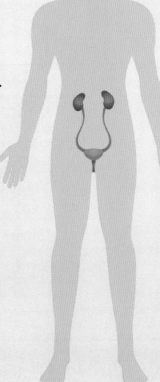

Cast of Characters:
Peter Kidney
Paul Kidney

Peter & Paul:
> Hello, and welcome to the Human Excretory System.
> We're the Kidney Brothers.

Peter:
> My name is Peter Kidney,

Paul:
> My name is Paul Kidney.

Peter & Paul:
> Yes Peter and Paul,
> but our friends just call us "THE P-P TWINS!"

Peter:
(Aside toward Paul)
> *Are they laughing at us?*

Paul:
(Aside toward Peter)
> *I'm...not...sure...*
> *But let's get on with it.*

(Back to audience)
> We are part of the excretory system of a human being by the name of Alexander Pic.
> Alexander is a normal human who does normal-human things.

Peter:
> He consumes and metabolizes nourishment.

Paul:
> He rids himself of metabolic waste.

Peter & Paul:

　　And he thinks about girls.

Peter:

　　Now we don't help him metabolize nourishment,
　　and we certainly don't help him with girls,
　　but we do help with waste, liquid waste, that is.
　　Solid waste is the responsibility of another system altogether.

Paul:
(Turning toward Peter)

　　Shall we recite the excretory poem?

Peter:
(To Paul)

　　Why not?

Peter & Paul:
(Reciting together and ending with a formal bow)

　　The Pee-not-Poo Poem
　　by Kanisha Kidney

　　Human beings make lots of waste,
　　it's nasty as can be.
　　The solid waste comes out as poo,
　　the liquid waste as pee.

　　And we excrete the liquid waste,
　　it's what we're made to do,
　　but solid waste is not our job
　　'cause we don't mess with poo.

Peter:

So this is how it works.
Alexander's body consumes stuff—
he breathes, he drinks, he eats.
Then all that stuff gets metabolized,
and all that metabolizing produces waste,
and somebody has to get rid of that waste.

Paul:

Which is where we come in: ALEXANDER'S EXCRETORY SYSTEM!
Now we kidneys are not Alexander's entire excretory system,
we're part of a whole team of organs that excrete waste.
His lungs exhale carbon dioxide waste,
his skin sweats lactic acid and sodium chloride.

Peter:

Salt?

Paul:

Yes, salt.
And his liver...
get ready, this is where we come in,
his liver converts ammonia into urea
which is then sent to us for disposal.

Peter:

So we really are a team,
and those other organs, the other members of the team?
Sure, they all excrete waste,
but they also do other stuff,
but we kidneys, the famous P-P Twins,
our work is about one thing and one thing only.
URINE!

Paul:

So here's what we do.
Are you ready?

Peter:

Let's do it!

Peter & Paul:

Step 1: We kidneys filter urea and uric acid and excess salt from the blood.

Step 2: Ureters carry the filtered material, or urine, to the urinary bladder.

Step 3: The urinary bladder stores all that urine,

otherwise Alexander would be peeing in his pants all day long.

And finally...

Step 4: Urine flows through the urethra and then...

The rush of mystic river.

An excretory dream.

Glory of the natural world.

Behold! THE GOLDEN STREAM!

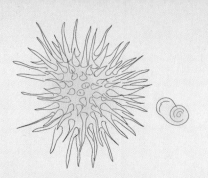

The Excretory Cheer

Stinky breath! Stinky sweat!
Stinky yellow pee!
Stinky stuff inside of you.
Stinky stuff in me.

Everybody ready?
Everybody shout -
THE EXCRETORY SYSTEM!
IT'S HOW WE GET IT OUT!

Stinky breath! Stinky sweat!
Stinky yellow pee!
Stinky stuff inside of you.
Stinky stuff in me.

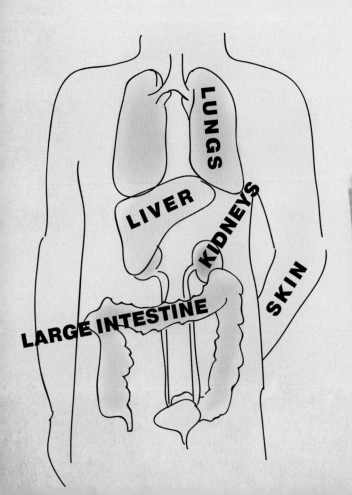

This little poem might help you remember the main organs that do the work of the excretory system: "stinky breath," the lungs; "stinky sweat," the skin; and "stinky yellow pee," the liver and kidneys. I could have included the large intestine in this poem, but I didn't because I think of it as the end of the digestive system, but it actually fits in both.

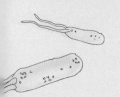
BACTERIA

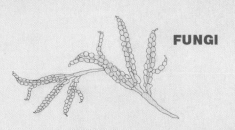
FUNGI

PARASITES

A Microscopic Request

Germs are here! Germs are there!
Germs are crawling everywhere!

I saw them in a microscope,
and now I use a lot of soap.
I wash my face, I wash my feet,
I wash my hands before I eat.

Germs are here! Germs are there!
Germs are crawling everywhere!

So this is what I now propose.
Get that finger out your nose!
And I don't want to scream and shout,
so please...DON'T PICK A BOOGER OUT!

Because...
GERMS ARE HERE!
GERMS ARE THERE!
GERMS ARE CRAWLING EVERYWHERE!

What we call "germs" are actually four different kinds of microorganisms: fungi, bacteria, parasites, and viruses. Germs are all around us, almost everywhere, so it's a good thing that they're so small. Imagine what your classroom would look like if germs were big enough to see without a microscope. Ahhhhhhh!

Mother Knows Best
A Play In One Act

Cast of Characters:
Child Flu Virus
Mother Flu Virus
Human Child

(Child Flu Virus and Mother Flu Virus stand center-stage, human child slightly off to one side.)

Child Flu Virus:
>Look, mom!
>A healthy child!
>This is my big chance.
>I'm going to hop right into her bloodstream
>and give that girl the flu.

Mother Flu Virus:
>Now you listen to me, Mr. Smarty-Pants.
>You better just keep your distance
>because that child is a human being,
>which means she has got an immune system,
>a whole network of cells and tissues and organs,
>all working together,
>prowling day and night like a pack of wolves.
>They're looking for—
>>fungi that can give her a rash and make her toes itch,
>>bacteria like strep that can give her a sore throat,
>>parasites like Giardia that can make her vomit
>>and poop like a faucet open at both ends,
>>and they are especially looking for a big-talking flu virus
>>just like you.

23

Child Flu Virus:

Mom, you talk about her immune system
like it's a virus-eating dragon.

Mother Flu Virus:

That's exactly what it's like,
but it's not just one virus-eating dragon,
it's a whole flock of virus-eating dragons,
and they're all working together.
That blood stream you want to "just hop into"
is full of white blood cells they call leukocytes.
They spot you,
they tag you,
they call for backup,
they gobble you up like hot-buttered popcorn,
and they remember you
so next time one of us comes around
they can jump us even quicker.

Child Flu Virus:

But what if her immune system is a little weak?
What if her leukocytes don't even notice me until it's too late?

Mother Flu Virus:
Weak?!
Now that's some mighty wishful thinking.
Why that little girl eats right,
she sleeps right,
she gets lots of exercise,
she washes her hands every chance she gets,
she never picks her nose,
and as if all that's not enough
she gets a flu-shot every year
and has had every kind of vaccination there is.
Her bone marrow and her lymph nodes and her spleen,
all swirling with antibodies
like a school of hungry Piranha fish.

Child Flu Virus:
Mom, I'm all grown up now,
I'm a flu virus,
and infecting people is what I'm suppose to do.
It's my duty, plain and simple,
and nothing you say is going to scare me away.
So...HERE I GO!

(Child Flu Virus charges off stage. Five seconds of silence as Mother Flu Virus wrings her hands in worry. Then from off stage.)

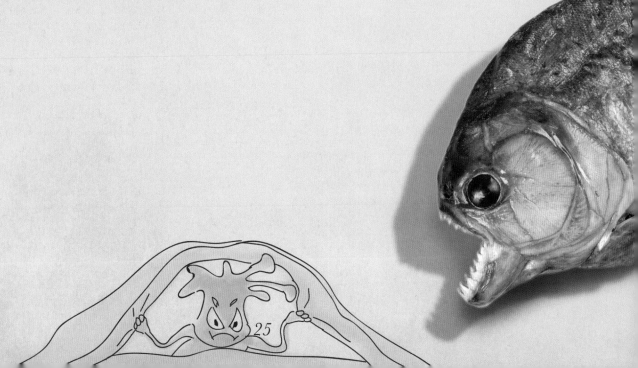

25

Child Flu Virus:
> What is that?!
> OH-NO!
> Ahhhhhhhhhhhhhhhhh!

(Child Flu Virus comes back on stage tattered and bandaged. He stands next to Mother Flu Virus as Human Child recites the epilogue.)

Human Child:
> In marrow bone, lymph nodes, and spleen
> my leukocytes are really mean.
> If you're a pathogenic germ,
> my leukocytes will make you squirm.
> Dragon! Wolf! Piranha fish!
> This system has a single wish.
> Make me immune! Oh yes-siree!
> That's what this system does for me.

Here's a little more information about "leukocytes." As you probably already know, human beings have red blood cells and white blood cells. White blood cells are produced in the marrow of our bones, and they're the germ-fighters. The term "leukocytes" is just another way of saying "white blood cells," and they come in two varieties: **phagocytes** (FAH-guh-sytes) and **lymphocytes** (LIM-fuh-sytes). **Phagocytes** are the ones that gobble up germs "like hot-buttered popcorn," and **lymphocytes** are the bloodstream police; the ones that remember a certain kind of germ so they can recognize it the next time it comes around. This produces what scientists call "adaptive immunity," and our body's ability to do this is what makes vaccinations work.

Hankie Hygiene

Oh my gosh! Excuse me please!
It feels like I'm about to sneeze.
Oh my goodness! Oh despair!
My germs will scatter everywhere.

I put my hand up to my face
to keep the world a healthy place.
And here it comes, a big A-CHOO!
Oh no! My hand is full of goo!

There's nothing wrong with mucus.
Mucus is a champ.
It keeps your nose from drying up
and keeps the tissue damp.

It also kills those dangerous germs
that float around in air,
so don't say it's disgusting
'cause it really isn't fair.

But all the same, when first you sniff,
go get a nice clean handkerchief,
and keep it ready on the spot,
so you won't spray your friends with snot.

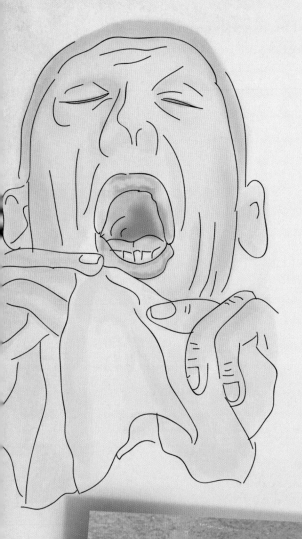

Healthy hygiene is a fairly new idea. Before the 1850's most people believed that disease was caused by "bad air," which they called the miasma theory. (Most doctors didn't even wash their hands when they did surgery or delivered babies.) Then along came germ theory which is the idea that some diseases are caused by germs. (How scientists proved it is one of the great stories of science. Check out John Snow, Louis Pasteur, and Robert Koch.) By 1900 scientists had identified more than twenty diseases caused by germs, one of which was tuberculosis. Now this is a very bad disease; it's estimated that by 1900 one out of every seven people who ever lived on earth had died of tuberculosis. So when scientists figured out that germs were the cause, we human beings went to war on germs and "hygiene" was our battle cry.

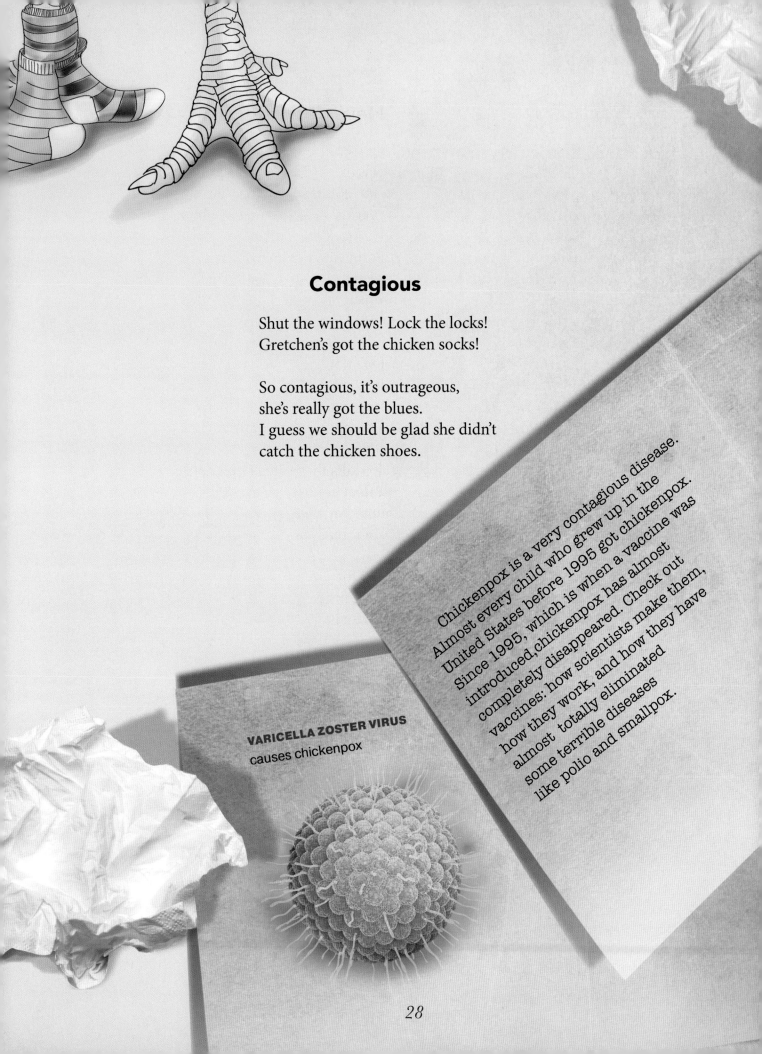

Contagious

Shut the windows! Lock the locks!
Gretchen's got the chicken socks!

So contagious, it's outrageous,
she's really got the blues.
I guess we should be glad she didn't
catch the chicken shoes.

VARICELLA ZOSTER VIRUS
causes chickenpox

Chickenpox is a very contagious disease. Almost every child who grew up in the United States before 1995 got chickenpox. Since 1995, which is when a vaccine was introduced, chickenpox has almost completely disappeared. Check out vaccines: how scientists make them, how they work, and how they have almost totally eliminated some terrible diseases like polio and smallpox.

28

E-mail, the Pony Express,
a Private Diary, and Revenge

I keep a private diary,
and last night I was making a very personal entry,
when my little brother interrupted me.
    "I have a test on the body," he said.
    "And I'm having trouble with the difference between
    the endocrine system and the nervous system.
    Please help me."
And he made his little-brother puppy-dog face,
so I told him I would say it one time,
and that he better listen closely
'cause I was not going to say it twice.

"Both systems are about messages between brain and body," I explained.
"But endocrine system messages are like letters in the Pony Express,
and nervous system messages are like E-mail on the internet.
So here it is:
    In the endocrine system
    messages are slow-acting
    in the form of chemical hormones excreted from glands,
    carried in blood through the circulatory system,
    and distributed broadly throughout the body.

    In the nervous system
    messages are fast-acting
    in the form of electrical impulses generated in neuron cells,
    traveling from cell to cell,
    and targeted to very specific areas of the body."

Which is when he said how the nervous system uses chemicals, too,
in the form of neurotransmitters that move its electrical impulses
across the synaptic gaps between neurons.

He said it like he totally knew it,
like he knew it so well he didn't even have to think about it,
which is when I realized that he wasn't thinking about it,
because his eyes were focused on my diary,
and I realized the whole thing was a trick
so the little brat could read my private stuff."

I did not squish him like a bug,
I didn't even rat-him-out to mom.
I simply closed my diary and said.
    "Someday you'll grow up and fall in love,
    which is when my revenge will accrue.
    Neither hormone nor neuron will serve to protect
    from the things I'll tell her about you."

Your endocrine glands make hormones that go into your bloodstream and travel all over your body to keep it in homeostasis, which you'll learn more about in the next poem. You also have exocrine glands that make substances that do not go into your bloodstream but instead flow out on the surface of an organ to do a local job. Some examples of exocrine glands are: sweat glands which send sweat to the surface of your skin to cool it; lacrimal glands which spread tears over your eyeballs to keep them lubricated; salivary glands squirt saliva to keep your mouth moist and help you digest food.
    And in case you're one of those learners who just have to get the whole picture, yes, there are different kinds of exocrine glands, three of them, but you're going to have to learn about them on your own because I have run out of space.

My Noble Glands
or
Homeostasis in the Kingdom of Me

Glands and hormones, hormones and glands,
constantly sending their bio-commands.
Like nobles who serve in the castles of kings,
they regulate all of my bodily things.

Baron Pituitary. You're truly the master.
Without you my life would be total disaster.
Now don't be so humble, you know that it's true,
my other glands mostly take orders from you.

Countess Thyroid, my dear, your power is sweet
making energy out of the food that I eat.
You metabolize food from my plate and my cup
breaking all of it down and then building me up.

My dear Duke Adrenal, you help me let loose.
When I've got to get going, you give me the juice.
Like a cowboy on horseback a-cracking his whip,
you get my attention and fill me with zip.

Sir Pancreas, yes you are truly a knight.
Without you my glucose would shoot out of sight.
Like gyroscopes working on ships out in space,
you keep it from zapping all over the place.

Lady Ovary! Lord Testis! Royal genders at truce.
Without you our bodies could not reproduce.
Yet oh how we humans in number have grown—
estrogen meets testosterone.

Glands and hormones, hormones and glands,
constantly sending their bio-commands,
adjusting my state on an hourly basis,
keeping my body in homeostasis.

Homeostasis refers to your body's ability to maintain a constant internal state in response to changing circumstances. It comes from two Greek words. The first part comes from **homoios** (ὅμοιος) which means *the same*. The second part comes from **stasis** (στάσις) which means *standing still*.

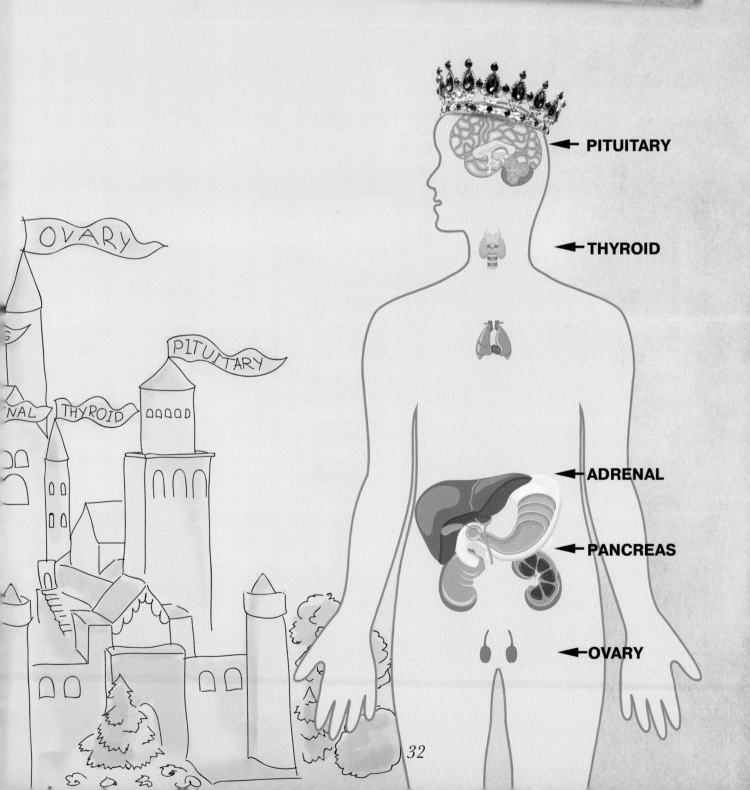

← **PITUITARY**

← **THYROID**

← **ADRENAL**

← **PANCREAS**

←**OVARY**

Neurotransmitter Nuisance
or
The Spark of Love

Something very strange happened this morning,
but I think I've figured it out.
    My skin is full of nerve cells they call neurons,
    and when something touches it
    those neurons generate an electrical impulse,
    and that electrical impulse wants to travel from neuron to neuron,
    but there's this tiny synaptic gap between my neurons
    so at the end of each neuron
    the electrical impulse produces a chemical called a neurotransmitter
    that lets the electricity jump the gap
    thus transmitting it from neuron to neuron,
    ending up in my brain,
    which interprets the message
    and immediately orders my body to respond.
All of which explains what happened this morning.

After first period I was standing at my locker
and Daisy May Maxamilian came walking up to me.
    Daisy May Maxamilian—
    black hair, hazel eyes, strawberry lips—
    she smiled, said hello,
    brushed the tips of her fingers against the skin of my cheek,
    and walked away.

Which is when it happened:
    An electrical impulse in my neurons,
    neurotransmitters zap it across synaptic gaps,
    it travels from neuron to neuron
    a surge that thunders into my defenseless fifteen year-old brain
    and hits me like a bolt of lightning.

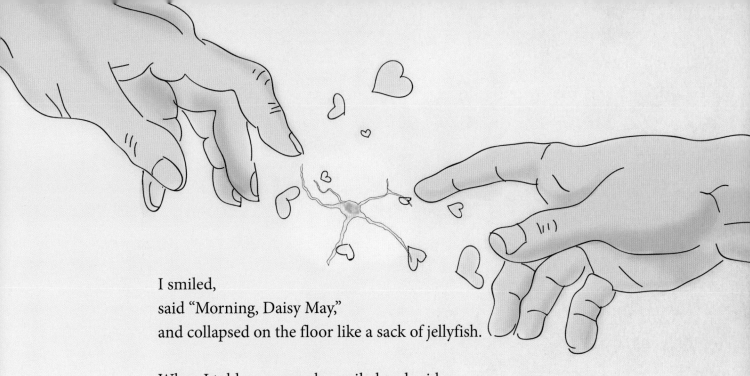

I smiled,
said "Morning, Daisy May,"
and collapsed on the floor like a sack of jellyfish.

When I told my mom she smiled and said,
"There's just one thing to say.
Those neurotransmitters are a dangerous thing
with a girl like Daisy May.

A neuron is a nerve cell. You have about 80 billion of them in your brain alone, and each one is like a little electrical generator. (If all the neurons in your brain fired at the same time they would make enough electricity to power a smart phone.)

So your neurons generate electrical impulses and carry them all over your body, but they'renot like electrical wires because neuron cells don't actually touch. Between each neuron cell there's a "synaptic gap" so each neuron has to activate neurotransmitters that can jump the gap and deliver the impulse to the next neuron. (This neurotransmitter activation is a complex chemical process, so don't worry if you don't understand it from the little I've said here. There are scientists who spend their lives studying how this works. And who knows, maybe someday you'll be one of them.)

So here's generally how the whole thing happens. You put the tip of your finger on a very hot plate, neurons in your finger generate an electrical impulse, the electrical impulse travels to the other end of the neuron and activates neurotransmitters that jump the gap and cause an electrical impulse in the next neuron, which happens over and over again, millions of times in less than the blink of an eye, until the impulse gets to your brain causing you to remove your finger from the hot plate and scream, "OUCH!"

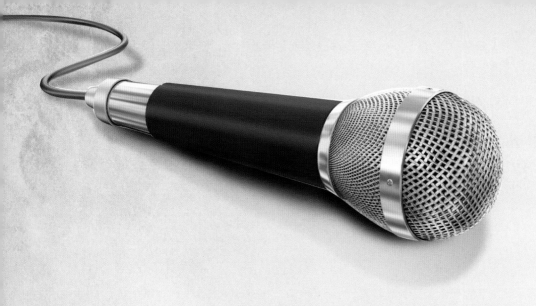

Brain Dance

A Play In One Act

Cast of Characters:
   Talk show host: C.T. Scan
   Main Guest: Miss Medulla Oblongata
   Other Guest: Cynthia Cerebrum
   Sheila Cerebellum
   Henrietta Hypothalamus
   Pauline Pituitary

(C.T. Scan, host of TV show Your Body—Inside and Out, is seated at a desk conducting an interview with Miss Medulla Oblongata.)

   C.T. Scan:
         Good evening, ladies and gentlemen,
         this is C.T. Scan,
         and welcome to another edition of *Your Body—Inside and Out*.
         For this evening's interview
         we have gone to the lower third of the human brainstem
         where we will meet Miss Always-on-the-Job herself,
         that workaholic of the human anatomy,
         Miss Medulla Oblongata.
(Turning to his guest)
         Hello, Miss Oblongata,
         and welcome to *Your Body—Inside and Out*.

Medulla:
(Unemotional, person of few words)
> Happy to be here, C.T.,
> and please,
> my friends just call me Medulla.

C.T. Scan:
> Friends, indeed.
> You medullas are friends to every human being who ever lived.
> Without you none of us would last a single day,
> yet historically,
> we hardly know you exist.
> You're the unsung heroes of the human anatomy.

Medulla:
> I do my job, sir.

C.T. Scan:
> Yes, and what a job it is.
> Breathing, for example.
> We humans can't live without breathing,
> but we don't even think about it.
> We just do it automatically,
> and it's all because of you.

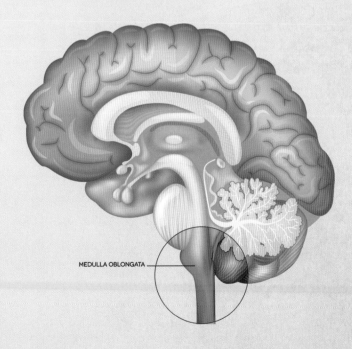

MEDULLA OBLONGATA

Medulla:
Yes, sir.
Breathing is part of my job.

C.T. Scan:
So tell us, what else is your job?

Medulla:
Well, to keep itself alive
a human body has to do a lot of stuff all at the same time.
The diaphragm muscle has to move air in and out of your lungs
about a thousand times an hour.
Who makes that happen? The Medulla.
The heart muscle has to compress to pump blood
about 5,000 times an hour.
Who makes that happen? The Medulla.
And don't get me started about all the work I do
after you eat a meal.

C.T. Scan:
And it's all involuntary.
Your body never has to think to do all those things.

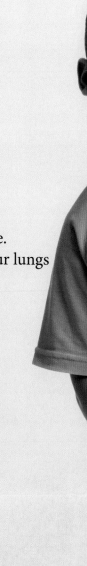

37

Medulla:

Think?
C.T. I regulate the body of a one Quanesha Jones.
Quanesha is 16 years old,
the goalie on her soccer team,
gets good grades, likes to dance,
and lately is absolutely crazy about a boy named Tyrell.
So last night at the school dance,
Tyrell walks up to Quanesha
with this big-ole smile on his face and says,
"Come on girl, LET'S DANCE!"
And Quanesha was just standing there
thinking hard about what to say next.
If she had to think about breathing and making her heart beat
she'd have just dropped down dead on the spot.
So I do it all for her.

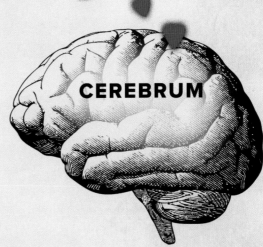

CEREBRUM

C.T. Scan:

That's pretty important stuff.

Medulla:

Yes it is important, C.T.
but everything her brain does is important,
and I'm just part of her brainstem,
and her brainstem is just one
of a whole bunch of important regions of Quanesha's brain.
And every one of us is doing important stuff day and night,
and day and night we are all working together as a team.

C.T. Scan:
> So the famous Medulla Oblongata is just part of her brainstem,
> and that brainstem
> is just one of a whole bunch of important
> regions of Quanesha's brain.

Medulla:
(Sarcastic, looking around as if searching for the source of an echo)
> There must be an echo around here?

C.T. Scan:
> Ah...yes.
> Well, what do you say we get the others out here?

(C.T. stands)
> Ladies and gentlemen, help me welcome
> the regions of Quanesha's brain.

(As C.T. introduces the new guests, each comes on stage waving at the audience and takes their seats beside Medulla. Each of them could be carrying a poster or a drawing of some kind to indicate their location in the brain.)

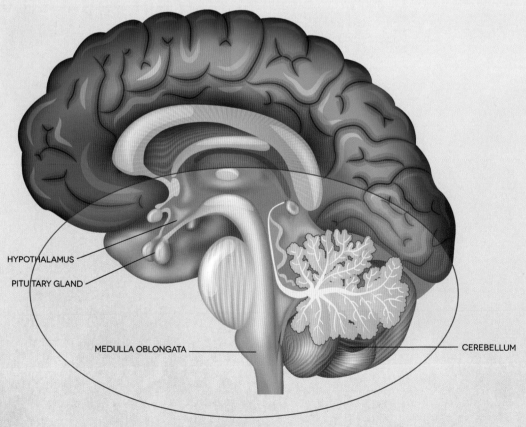

HYPOTHALAMUS

PITUITARY GLAND

MEDULLA OBLONGATA

CEREBELLUM

Thought Boss Cynthia Cerebrum!

(Clapping...)

Coordination Queen Sheila Cerebellum!

(Clapping...)

Madam Electro-Chemical Liaison Henrietta Hypothalamus!

(Clapping...)

And last but not least,
Boss Gland Pauline Pituitary!

(Clapping...)

Thank all of you for coming.
Now, why don't each of you tell our audience about your work.
I know that each of your jobs is complicated
and we could be here all night,
so try as best you can to keep it short and sweet.

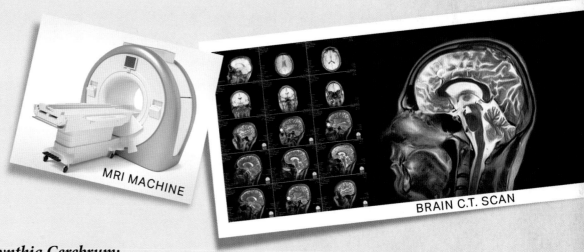

MRI MACHINE

BRAIN C.T. SCAN

Cynthia Cerebrum:

I guess I should start.
My name is Cynthia Cerebrum,
and if I say so myself,
I'm more or less the thought boss.
I do all of Quanesha's thinking,
I keep her memories,
and I handle all of her voluntary muscle movements.
So last night, when Tyrell asked her to dance,
I told her to answer by saying,
"Tyrell, where'd you learn your manners?
You better try asking again,
and this time be polite and make your Mama proud."

(All the brain regions laugh and say to each other, "That's right that's exactly what she said. Ah-hum.")

40

Sheila Cerebellum:

My name is Sheila Cerebellum,
and last night as soon as Quanesha started dancing
I got to working overtime keeping her balanced
so she didn't fall flat on her face on that dance floor.
I'm the one who keeps all her muscles working together
so Tyrell couldn't help but think
how she looked like some African goddess.

(All the brain regions laugh and say, "That's right that's exactly how he was looking at her. Ah-hum.")

41

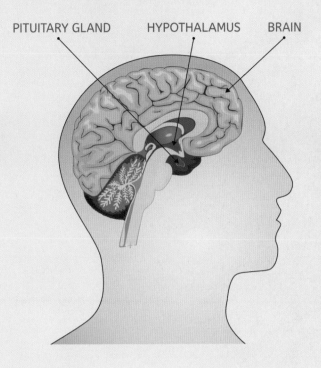

PITUITARY GLAND   HYPOTHALAMUS   BRAIN

Henrietta Hypothalamus:

Well my name is Henrietta Hypothalamus,
and I know I'm only the size of an almond,
and all you nice folks are probably thinking—
How can something so small do anything important?
Well you just ask my friends here,

**(All brain regions emphatically shaking
their heads in an up-and-down affirmative)**

I'm the link between Quanesha's nervous system and her endocrine systems,
and that nervous system brings me information
about what Quanesha's body is needing,
so I send my special stop or start hormones to my colleague, Miss Pituitary,
which tell her what she needs to do.
And the whole time I'm doing that
I'm also watching over Quanesha's heart rate
and blood pressure and body temperature,
which I like to keep at a nice 98.6 degrees Fahrenheit,
so last night if it weren't for me
that sweet child would have been overheating
like a 1960's muscle car with a broken radiator.

**(All brain regions laugh and say, "Now that's a fact, that girl would have
been steaming something awful.")**

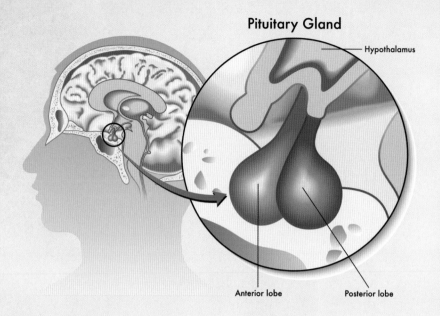

Pituitary Gland

Hypothalamus

Anterior lobe

Posterior lobe

Pauline Pituitary:
 Well if you thought Miss Hypothalmus was small,
 just take a look at me.
 I'm not but the size of a little-ole green pea,
 but my Mama always told me,
 "Good things come in small packages."
 And you know that's true because here I am.
 My name is Pauline Pituitary,
 but I am known to my friends as "Boss Gland."

(All brain regions emphatically shaking their heads in an up-and-down affirmative saying, "She's the boss all right. Just ask those other glands.")

Pauline Pituitary:
 You see,
 stimulated by those stop or start hormones I get from Miss Hypothalamus,
 I send instructions to every other gland in Quanesha's body,
 but I also have my own work
 because I produce all of Quanesha's growth hormones.
(Laughing to herself)
 So you see, I'm the one responsible for that whole dancing thing last night
 'cause it's mostly 'cause of me
 that Quanesha is going through puberty
 which is why she thinks Tyrell is the sweetest boy in the world
 when just last year she thought he smelled like dirty socks.

Well it looks like our time is up.
Thank you all for being with us tonight on
Your Body—Inside and Out.
Please tune in next week for our special guest
the Human Colon,
when we will be exploring that famous colon motto,
"It's a dirty job, but somebody's got to do it."

There's a lot more to know about the brain than what's in this play. There's the thalamus just above the hypothalamus, the midbrain and pons which are the two other parts of the brainstem right above the medulla, the cortex which is actually part of the cerebrum. And there are a whole bunch of lobes and subsections all doing different stuff. When I started learning about the brain I felt lost in a maze, but once I learned the parts in this play, it got easier for me to understand the rest. So the more you learn, the easier it gets.

Sense Alive

Senses, senses, I have five.
Senses make me feel alive.
     Everybody look at me,
     I have eyes that let me see.

Senses, senses, I have five.
Senses make me feel alive.
     Listen, listen, I can hear
     giggle noises in my ear.

Senses, senses, I have five.
Senses make me feel alive.
     I can touch, I can feel,
     everything I touch is real.

Senses, senses, I have five.
Senses make me feel alive.
     I want candy, I can't wait,
     chocolate candy tastes just great.

Senses, senses, I have five.
Senses make me feel alive.
     In the bathroom Daddy goes…
     WISH I DIDN'T HAVE A NOSE!

Senses, senses, I have five.
Senses make me feel alive.

Every computer has one or more input device like a keyboard or a mouse or a scanner, something by which we put information into the computer. If your brain were a computer, your five senses would be your input devices. Everything you know, directly or indirectly, gets into your brain through one or more of your senses.

You might be interested to know that some neuroscientists argue that we have more than five senses, some think as many as 33. This is the kind of thing you might want to check out. Who knows? You may be the scientist who someday definitively proves that we do have more than five senses. Or maybe you'll be the one to prove that five is the number and that we were right all along.

SEE

TOUCH

SMELL

TASTE

HEAR

A Booty-ful Part
or
The Dance of Life

My skeleton? A bunch of bones
with marrow at the core.
Without it I would be a blob
that rolls around the floor.

Brainstem? Cerebrum?
Cerebellum too?
The brainy parts inside my head
that help me think of you.

Two big spongy lungs,
arteries and veins
to keep my body working
when my muscles start to strain.

Eyes and ears and arms and legs,
and if you're not a snooty,
my very favorite body part—
THE MIGHTY HUMAN BOOTY!

Three gluteal muscles,
the strongest in my body,
which also work as padding when
I'm sitting on the potty.

Live without a booty?
I wouldn't take a chance,
because my favorite thing to do
is shake it when I dance.

Take care of your body, keep your
brain thinking all the time, open
your senses to the joys of life, and
please-please-please...
DON'T...FORGET...TO DANCE.

47

An Invitation

Some years ago it became my life's dream to write a bunch of poems about science; poems that would be both fun and instructional; poems to simultaneously entertain you and help you become life-long learners.

I've been at it now for over 20 years, and I have begun to understand that this little book and the ones to follow, are just a first step, and that the next step depends on you.

That's why I am inviting you to join me in the wonderful work of awakening the joy of powerful thinking in the minds of your generation. We humans are proud of our tall buildings and our 2000 year old aqueducts and our 4000 year old pyramids, and we should be. But what we can be most proud of is that pocketful of simple yet powerful ideas that made every one of those things possible. I invite you to join me in helping to keep those ideas healthy and strong among your generation.

Look back through the pages of this book, pick out a piece that you really like, and then do something with it and send it to me. You might make a video of you and your friends performing it; or create your own original illustration or animation; or write your own original poem or play; or simply write your thoughts after reading it; or maybe something else I can't even imagine. As time goes by we at Brod Bagert's HeART of Science will be selecting some of your material and (with your permission) sharing it with others just like you.

I believe that many of you will accept this invitation and have fun doing it. There may even be a few of you who will like it a lot, a few of you for whom it will become the joy of your lives, as it has been of mine. Maybe you'll be the ones to help take the idea behind Brod Bagert's HeART of Science to a whole new level. And maybe, eventually, you'll become the stars that bring light to the night skies of your generation. Please accept this as your invitation.

Dedication

To my wonderful grandson, Isaiah.
B.B.

To my amazing son, Derek.
N.K.

Publishing Information

Published by Living Road Press
San Antonio, TX

ISBN 978-1732151529

Acknowledgement

Thanks to Alan Burshell, M. D., for giving this manuscript a critical read and for giving its author a much needed dose of encouragement.